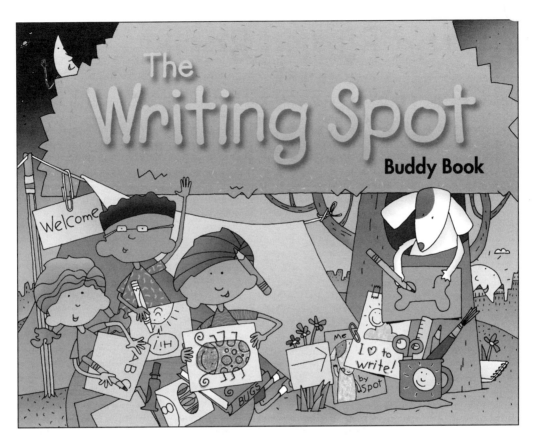

The Writing Spot

Buddy Book

. . . a resource of student activities
to accompany *The Writing Spot Big Book*

WRITE SOURCE®

GREAT SOURCE EDUCATION GROUP
a Houghton Mifflin Company
Wilmington, Massachusetts

About the Buddy Book . . .

The Buddy Book is a place to write and draw. It has two sections, "Writer's Response/Guided Writing Skills" and "The Alphabet Pages." The pages go with the pages in *The Writing Spot Big Book*.

Printed in the United States of America

International Standard Book Number: 978-0-669-49328-3

0-669-49328-7

7 8 9 10 -0877- 11

4500295907

Table of Contents

Writer's Response/Guided Writing Skills

The Process of Writing

Writer's Response/Guided Writing Skills

1

Writer's Response: Draw your writing spot. Add words or pictures for things you like to write about.

Spot writes.

Writers follow steps when they write.

Trace these steps for Spot to follow when he writes. Color the pictures.

START

look and think

talk and listen

read

share

write

Writer's Response: Draw and label some things you would like to look at and think about.

Writers look and think.

Writers think about letters and words.

Connect the letters from *a* to *o*. The first two have been connected for you. Add something to the picture. Trace circles around the two words and color the picture.

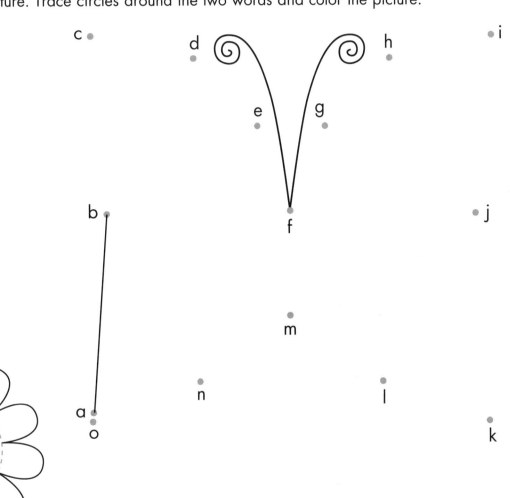

Writer's Response: Write or draw about things Spot might hear in your classroom.

Writers talk and listen.

Writers listen for letter sounds.

Listen for the sound of **b** at the beginning of the word **bubble**. Draw something that begins with the sound of **b** in each bubble. Add **b** words to this page.

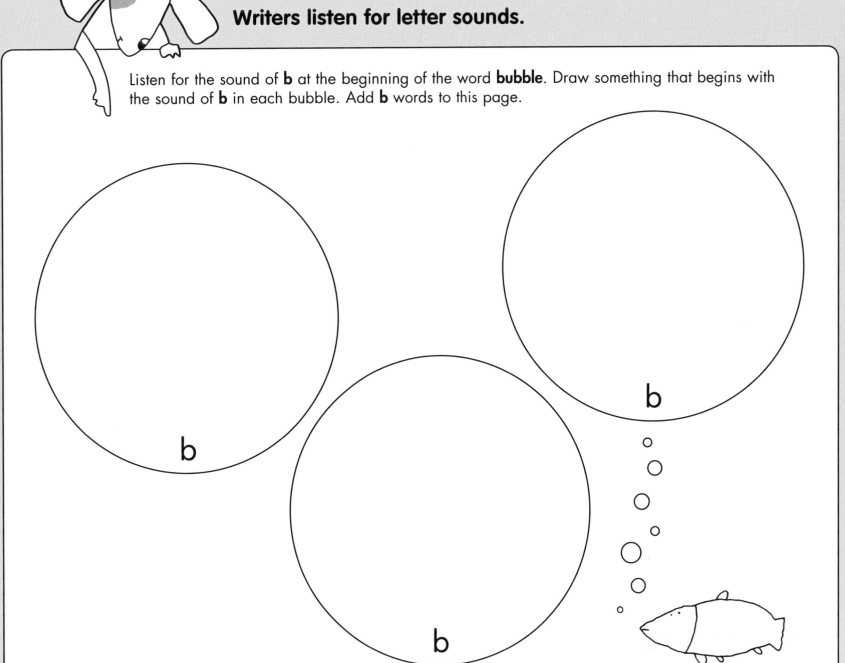

b

b

b

Writer's Response: Draw pictures and write words for a zoo book. Write a name (title) for your book.

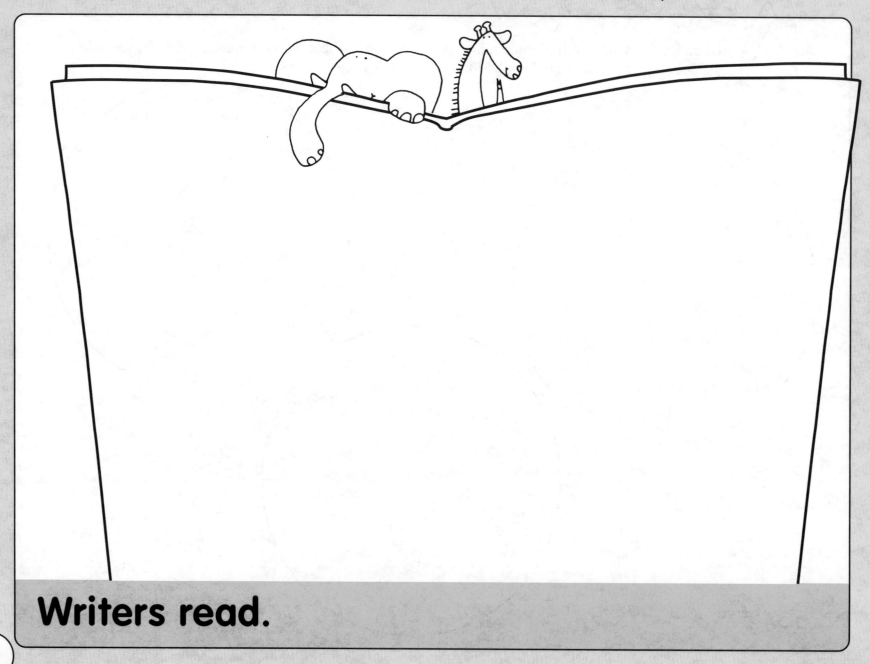

Writers read.

Writers read words using letter sounds.

Say the name of each picture. Circle the letter you hear first. Color the pictures.

l   s

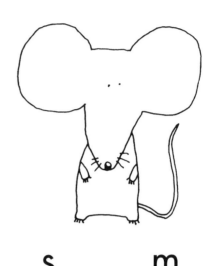

s   m

t   m

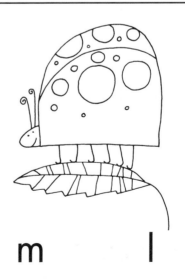

m   l

Writer's Response: Make a picture of your house. Write your name and address.

My House

My Name ____________________

My Address ____________________

____

Writers write.

Writers write words.

Write the name of a person, place, or thing after the word **my**. Draw a picture in each space.

This is my _____ .

This is my _____ .

Writer's Response: Draw pictures of people you like to share your writing with. Write their names.

Writers share.

Writers share made-up stories.

Write a name or a word on each blank. Then share your story.

One night _____ had a dream.
name of a boy/name of a girl

_____ saw a big whale.
He/She

Next _____ got on a boat.
name of a boy/name of a girl

Then _____ woke up.
he/she

13

Writers share weather stories.

Write words on the lines to complete this story.

windy   snowy   sunny   rainy

I like a _____ day.

wind blows   snow falls   sun shines   rain comes

I like days when the

_____ .

14

The Forms of Writing

Writer's Response/Guided Writing Skills

We send notes and cards.

Writers make notes for friends.

Connect the dots. Then write a friend's name on the line. Color the note and show it to your friend.

I like you,

_____

I do. I do.

17

Plants

sunflowers

lettuce

pumpkins

carrots

We make lists.

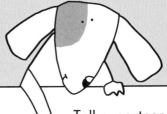

Writers make lists using words and pictures.

Tell a partner some things you wish for. Then fill this page with wish words and pictures.

19

We write in journals.

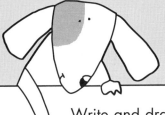

Writers write words and draw pictures in journals.

Write and draw on this journal page.

21

We tell and write stories.

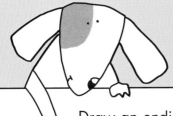

We tell a story with a beginning, a middle, and an ending.

Draw an ending for this story. Then tell the whole story. Write words for the story if you wish.

We make signs.

We make signs that show directions.

Write the correct word in each arrow.

↑ up　　↓ down　　← left　　→ right

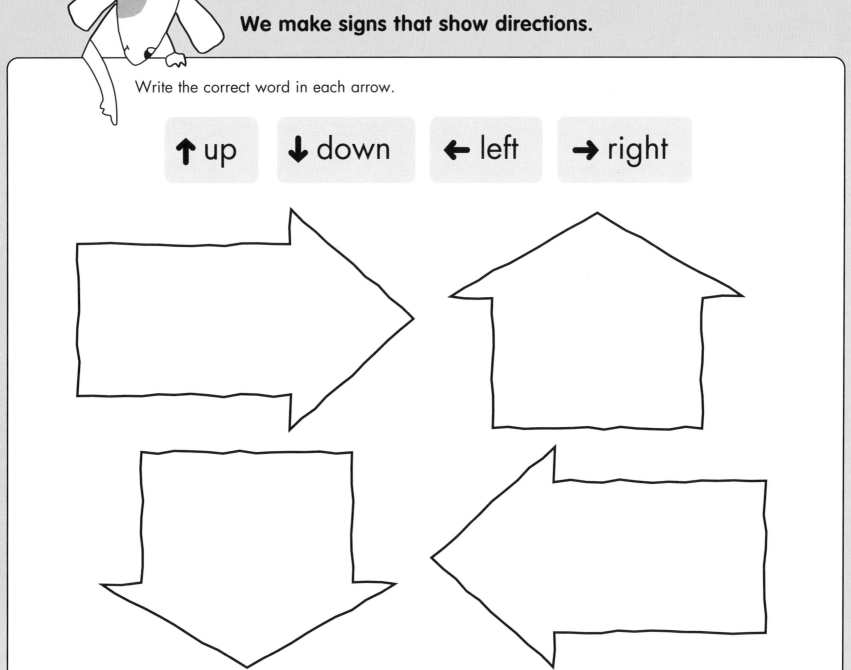

25

We make signs to label things.

Trace the words on the signs below. Color the pictures.

The Tools of Learning

Writer's Response: Color the keys for the letters in the words. Practice keyboarding the words.

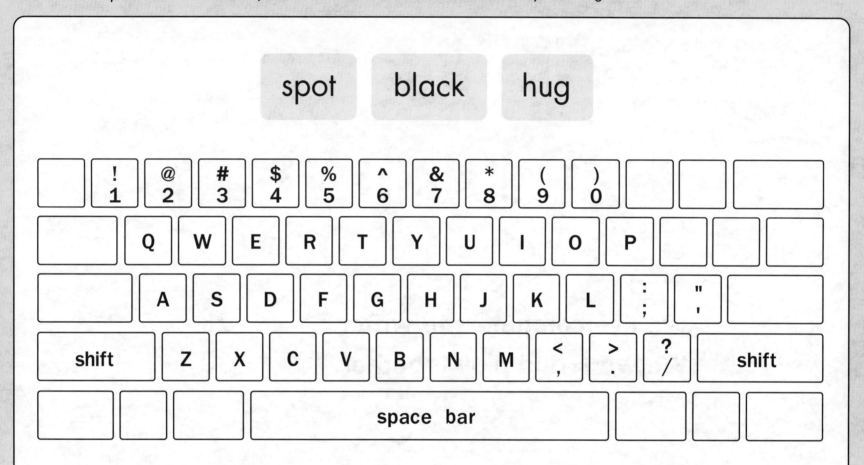

spot   black   hug

We use computers to write.

We use computers to write words and sentences.

Write three favorite words. Then write a sentence. Use a keyboard to type what you wrote.

1. _____

2. _____

3. _____

_____

_____

We work and play together.

We work together to write lists.

Talk with a partner about things that are inside and things that are outside. Make lists with words and pictures.

Inside

Outside

We play together to make words.

Use these letters to make some words. Take turns with a partner to make it a game.

a	b	c	d	e	f	g	h	i
j	k	l	m	n	o	p	q	r
s	t	u	v	w	x	y	z	

cat

_____   _____

_____   _____

_____   _____

Word Study/ Phonics

Writer's Response/Guided Writing Skills

Writers explore letters, sounds, and words.

34

Writers explore the beginning sounds and letters of words.

Say the name for each picture. Circle the letter for the sound you hear at the **beginning** of each word.

r　　w

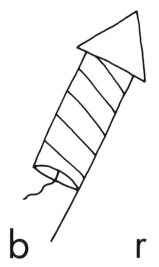

b　　r

b　　g

g　　w

Writers explore the ending sounds and letters of words.

Say the name for each picture. Circle the letter for the sound you hear at the **end** of each word.

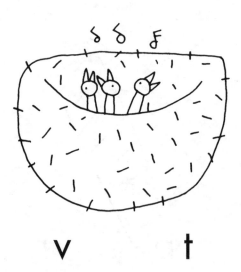

v   t

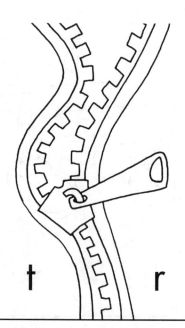

t   r

l   p

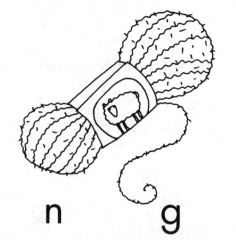

n   g

Writers use beginning sounds and letters to make words.

Use these beginning letters to make words from the alphabet chart. Draw pictures, too.

v   h   j   k   s   b

__ase

__ocks

__ite

__at

__acket

__ox

37

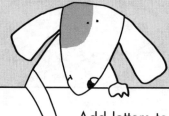

Writers use sounds and letters to finish words.

Add letters to finish the words. The words describe the silly pictures. Color the pictures.

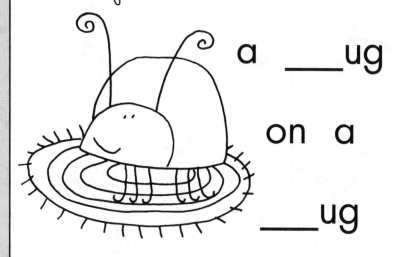

a ___ug

on a

___ug

a ___ig

on a

___ig

a ___og

on a

___og

a ___ish

on a

___ish

Writers explore words that end with the same sound.

Choose letters to make words for the **-et** word family. Add pictures for some of your words.

p   n   w   s   j   v   g

___et

___et

___et

___et

___et

net

Writer's Response: Add **at** to each line to make four words that rhyme with *hat*. Add your own pictures.

c_____

m_____

hat

r_____

b_____

Writers use letters to make words.

Writers enjoy making rhyming words.

Write **f** on each line to make rhyming words. Read these rhyming pairs with a partner. Then look at "Alligator to Zipper-Dee-Do!" to find other words that rhyme with these picture words.

bed

___ed

hat

___at

sea

___lea

snow

___low

sky

___ly

pull

___ull

41

Writers make lists of words.

List kinds of animals, favorite foods, or another category that interests you.
If you wish, add pictures to your list.

_____

_____

_____

_____

_____

_____

Writers match words to pictures.

Write the **-an** words for these pictures. Add a picture for another **-an** word.

f v p m t r

___an

___an

___an

___an

Writers use words to tell who people are.

Write the names of friends and family members to make two lists.

Friends

Family

Writers use words to tell where things are.

Trace the **where** words. Color the pictures.

on   in   behind   under

45

Writers use words to tell what color something is.

Color each picture with one of the listed colors. Write the correct **color** word on each line. Draw your own picture for one color.

red   blue   green   orange

_____

_____

_____

_____

Writers use words to tell how many.

Write the correct **number** word next to each number. Draw your own pictures to show how many.

two   four   one   three

1 _____

2 _____

3 _____

4 _____

47

Writers put words together in sentences.

Writers use words to write sentences.

Unscramble the puzzle pieces to write two sentences.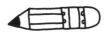

 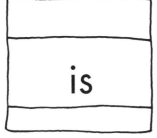  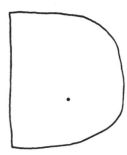

silly   is   Spot   .

Spot _____

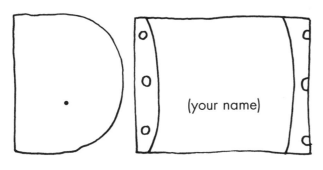  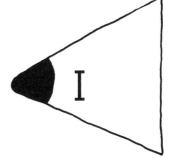

.   (your name)   am   I

_____

49

Writers use letters to write words and sentences.

Follow the directions.

Write one letter on each line.

_____ _____ _____ _____

Write two color words.

_____ _____

Write one sentence about a color.

_____

Writers use sentences to tell stories.

Use these words from the **-at** family to finish these sentences. Color the pictures.

mat   hat   cat   rat   Pat

_____ wrote a story. It told about

a _____ on a _____

and a _____ in a _____ .

51

Writers use sentences to write notes.

Add opposite words to complete this rhyming note. Color the pictures.

home	night	away	day	work	play

You like _night_ .   I like _____ .

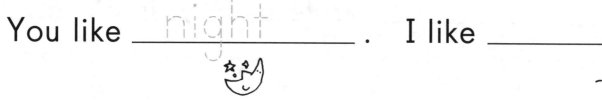

You like _____ .   I like _____ .

You like _____ .   I like _____ .

Writers use sentences to tell about something.

Color the frog green. Then choose words to tell about a frog.

green   four   jump   swim

This is a frog.

It is _____ .

Frogs have _____ legs.

They like to _____ and _____ .

53

Writer's Response: Read the poem. Color the pictures. Circle the part of the poem you like the best.

Alligator sits, Butterfly flits.

Cup of tea, Duck at sea.

Eggs to cook, Fish in a brook.

Girl named Mary, Hat for Harry.

Igloo white, Jacket bright.

Kite in the sky, Ladybug shy.

Mouse near a hole, Nest like a bowl.

Alligator to Zipper-Dee-Do!

Octopus below, Penguin in the snow.

 Quilt for a bed, Rocket that's red.

 Socks for running, Turtle goes sunning.

 Umbrella for showers, Vase full of flowers.

 Wagon to pull, Bo_x_ full of wool.

 Yarn soft and blue,

 Zipper-dee-do!

Writers use rhyming words.

Write **ish** on each line to make two words that rhyme with **fish.** Draw what you wish for in the dish.

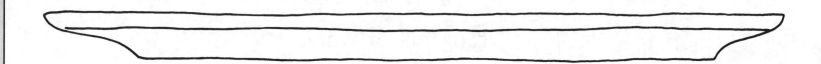

d_____

fish

w_____

Almanac/ Theme Pages

Writer's Response/Guided Writing Skills

Writer's Response: Write *Happy Birthday* and decorate this birthday banner.

Happy Birthday to you!

Write your birthday date.

Color your birthday month *yellow*. Use other colors for the rest of the months. Write your birthday month and date in the box.

January

February

March

April

May

June

July

August

September

October

November

December

My birthday date:

Writer's Response: Draw yourself and write a word that describes how you feel.

I feel . . .

Writers use words to tell feelings.

Color the faces. Write the correct feeling word under each face. Write your own feeling word to finish the sentence.

sad   happy   mad   sleepy

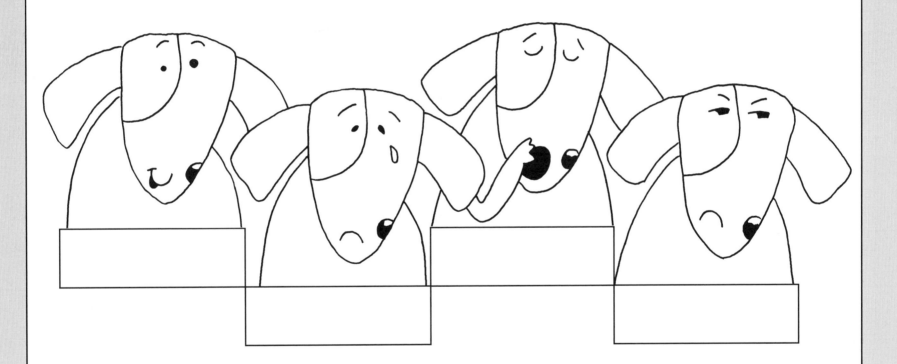

I am _____ .

61

Writer's Response: Draw some friends in the clubhouse and write their names.

_____'s
Clubhouse

Let's be friends.

Writers like to write their friends' names.

Write the names of five friends. Begin the names with capital letters. Draw your friends' faces if you wish.

1. _____

2. _____

3. _____

4. _____

5. _____

Writer's Response: Draw and label some healthful foods you'd like to eat.

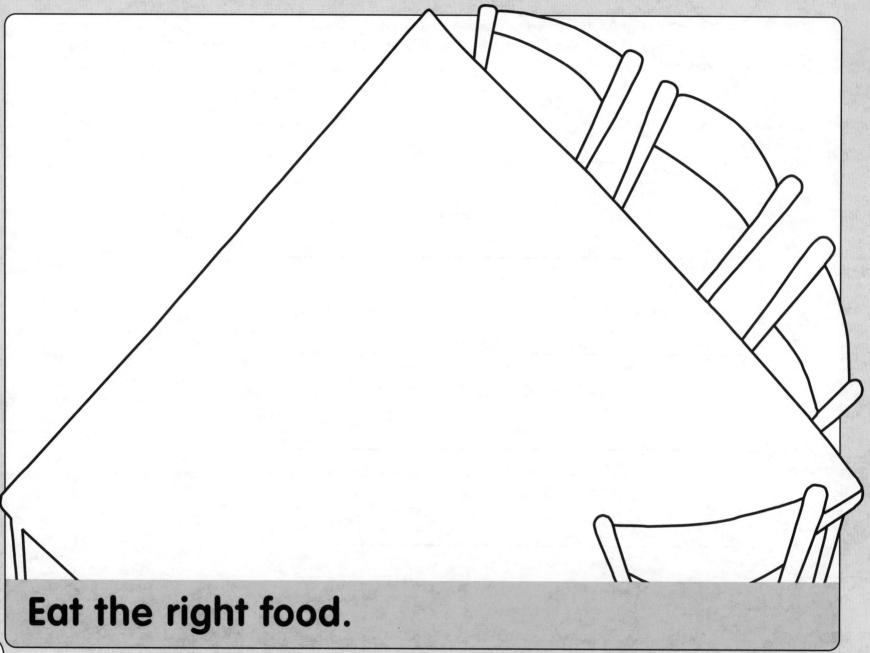

Eat the right food.

Writers listen for letter sounds.

Say the name of each food. Circle the letter that you hear first. Tell a partner which food names begin with the same sounds.

l   c   d

m   w   t

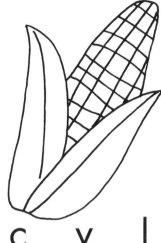

c   v   l

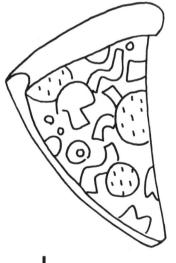

h   t   p

l   m   p

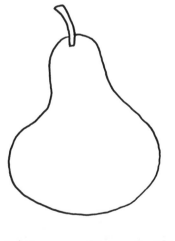

w   g   p

Water is everywhere.

Writers can say many things in sentences.

To make sentences, write the name of a person, a plant, or an animal on each blank. Add pictures.

Water helps _____.

Water helps _____.

Water helps _____.

67

Writer's Response: Put yourself in the space suit. Then draw and name a new planet.

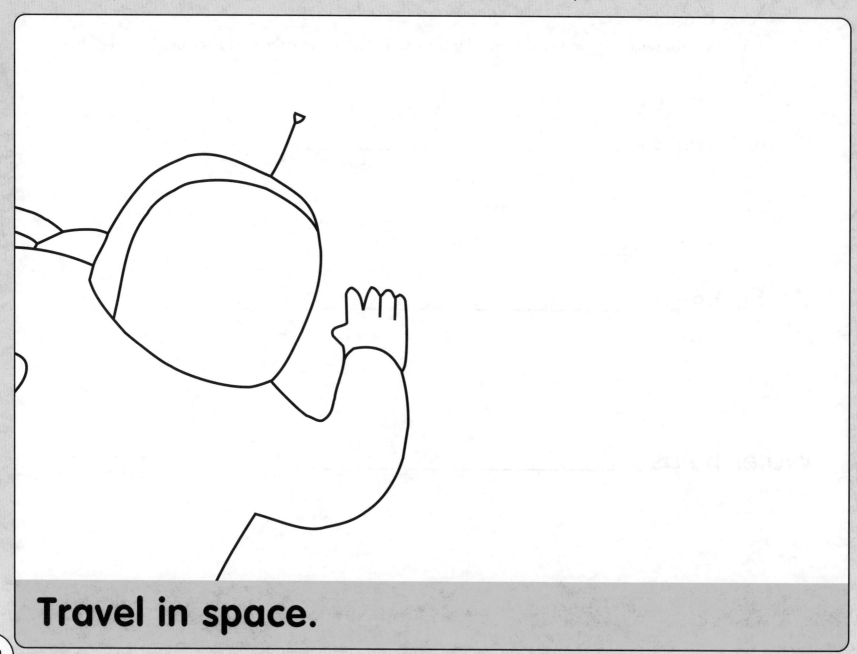

Travel in space.

Writers look for the letters in words.

Color the **Ss** words **yellow**. Color the **Mm** words **purple**. Color the **Pp** words **blue**.

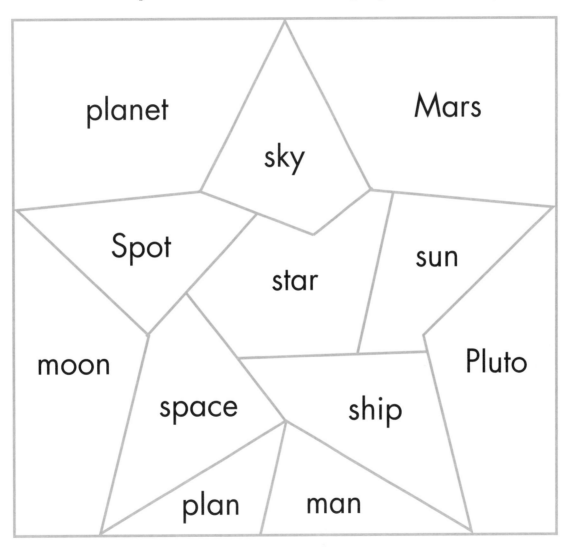

planet

Mars

sky

Spot

sun

star

moon

Pluto

space

ship

plan

man

Writer's Response: Draw yourself in the helicopter. Add a picture about weather and label it.

What's the weather?

Writers use special words to write about weather.

Draw lines from the weather words to the correct pictures. Draw your own picture for **hot**. Color the pictures.

windy

cold

rainy

hot

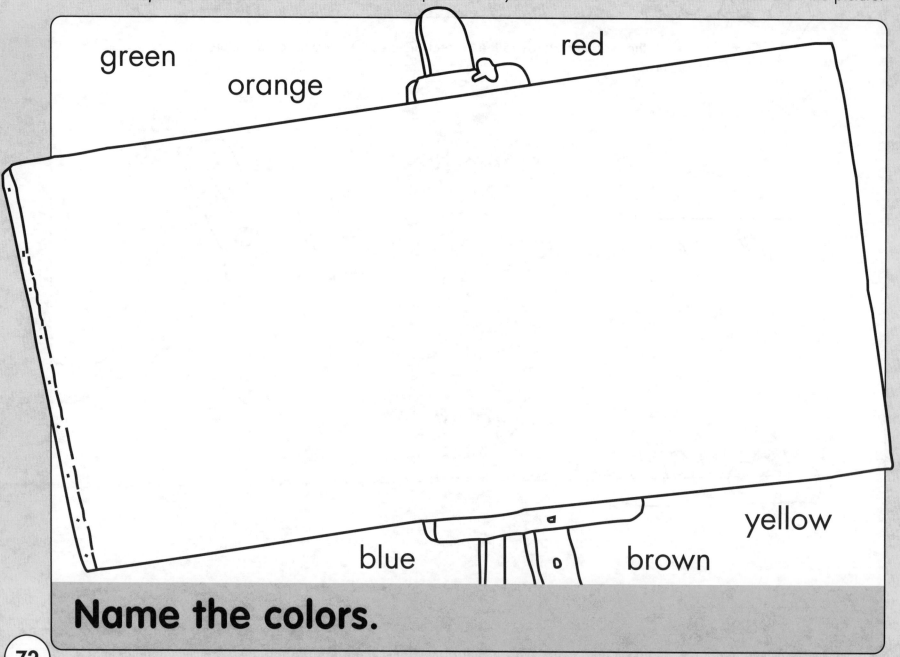

green

orange

red

blue

brown

yellow

Name the colors.

Writers follow directions using color words.

Color each picture with the color that is given.

blue

green

yellow

red

73

Listen to the rhyme.

Writers enjoy reading and writing rhyming words.

Connect the dots from 1 to 10. Then read the two lists of rhyming words with a partner. Write the correct word for the picture on the line at the bottom.

mat

rat

sat

cat

pat

bat

hat

fat

vat

9

2

10 · · 1

8 ·

· 3

7 ·

· 4

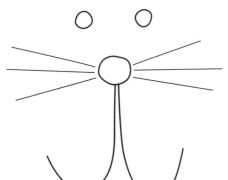

6

5 _____

75

Writer's Response: Draw and write the name of a pretend place you would like to visit.

Once upon a time . . .

Writers use words to tell stories.

Write **Spot** on each blank to finish these sentences. Then draw a picture to go with the story.

Spot

Spot and his friends like to play.

"I will hide," said _____ .

"I will find you, _____ ," said his friend.

Where is _____ hiding?

The Alphabet Pages

Alphabet Chart

Aa alligator	Bb butterfly	Cc cup	Dd duck	Ee eggs	Ff fish
Gg girl	Hh hat	Ii igloo	Jj jacket	Kk kite	Ll ladybug	Mm mouse
Nn nest	Oo octopus	Pp penguin	Qq quilt	Rr rocket	Ss socks
Tt turtle	Uu umbrella	Vv vase	Ww wagon	Xx bo<u>x</u>	Yy yarn	Zz zipper

Aa

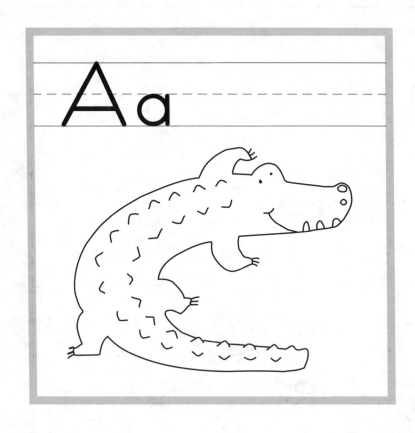

Alligator sits,

B b

Butterfly flits.

C c

Cup of tea,

Duck at sea.

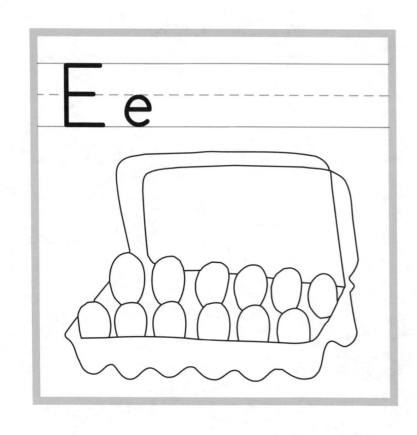

E e

Eggs to cook,

F f

Fish in a brook.

Girl named Mary,

Hat for Harry.

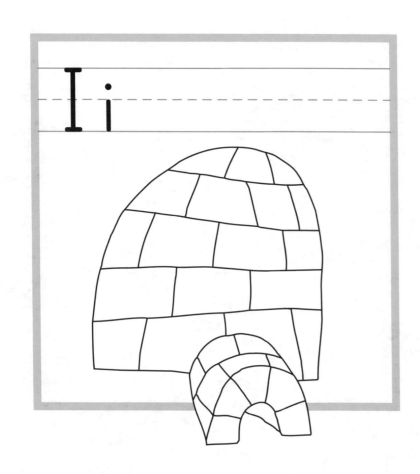

I i

Igloo white,

J j

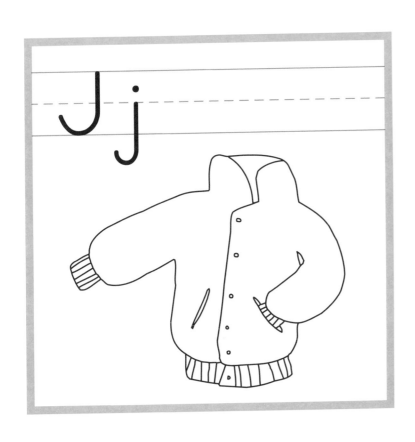

Jacket bright.

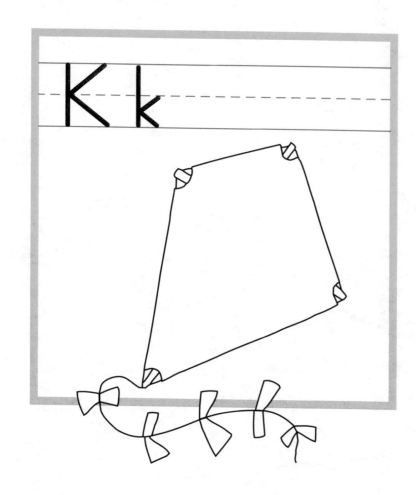

Kite in the sky,

L l

Ladybug shy.

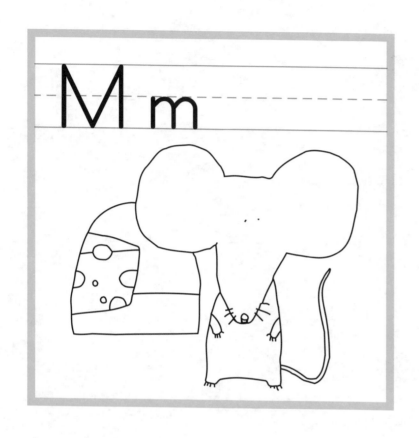

Mouse near a hole,

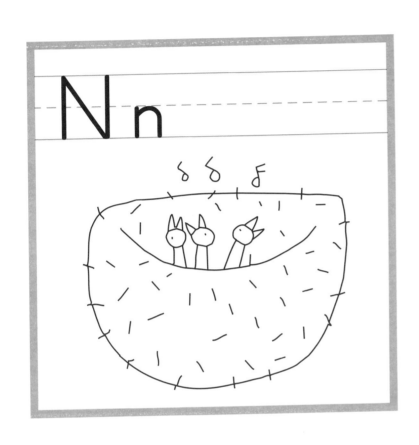

Nn

Nest like a bowl.

O o

Octopus below,

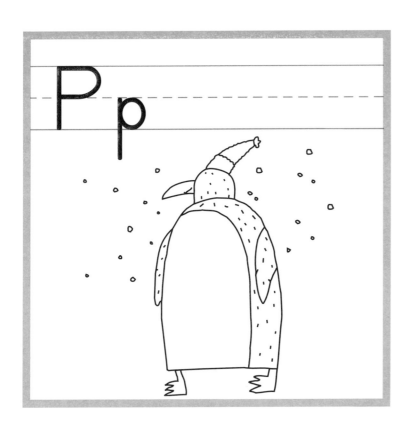

P p

Penguin in the snow.

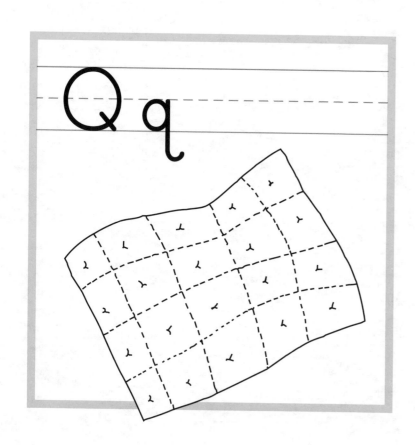

Qq

Quilt for a bed,

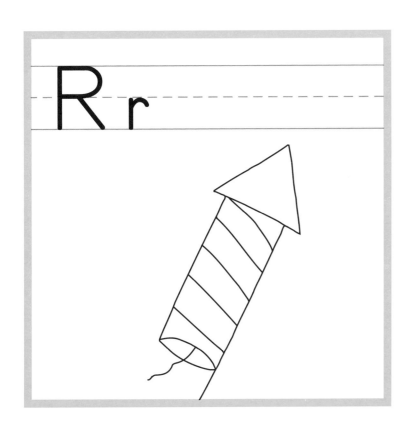

Rocket that's red.

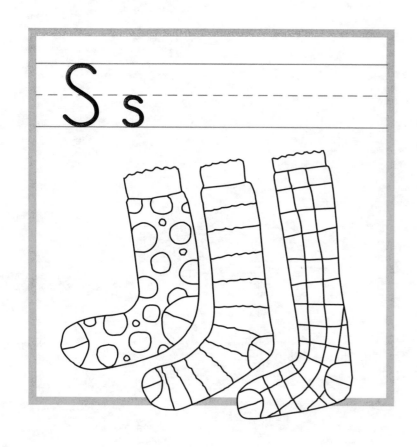

S s

Socks for running,

Turtle goes sunning.

U u

Umbrella for showers,

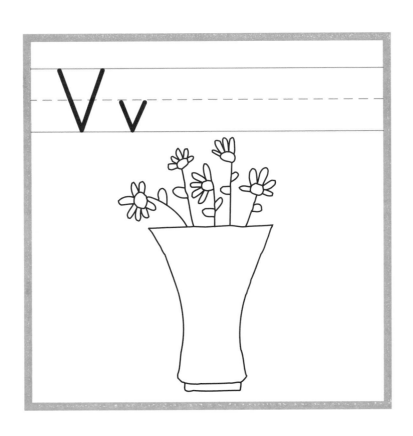

V v

Vase full of flowers.

W w

Wagon to pull,

X x

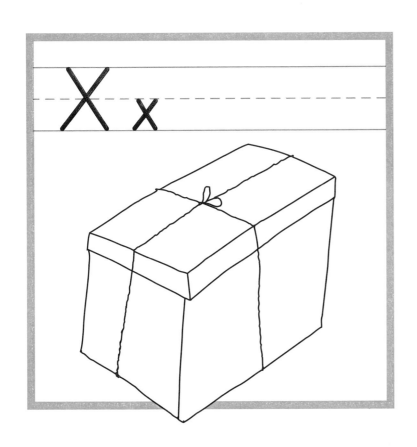

Bo<u>x</u> full of wool.

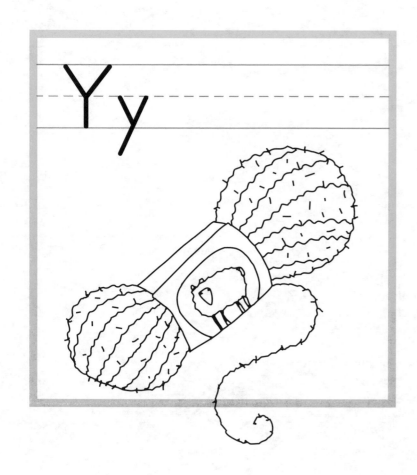

Yy

Yarn soft and blue,

Z z

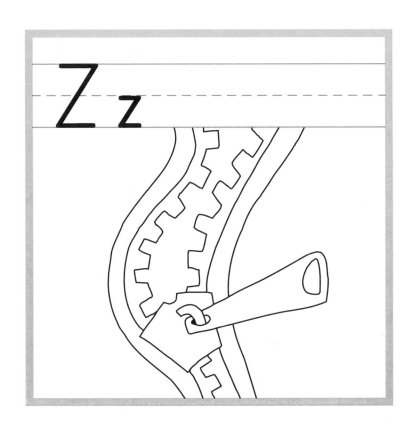

Zipper-dee-do!

a	come	happy	love	thank
am	dad	has	me	the
and	dear	have	mom	to
are	dog	he	mother	us
baby	family	house	my	was
boy	father	I	name	we
brother	for	in	no	with
but	friend	is	play	yes
came	girl	it	saw	you
can	good	like	she	
cat	had	look	sister	

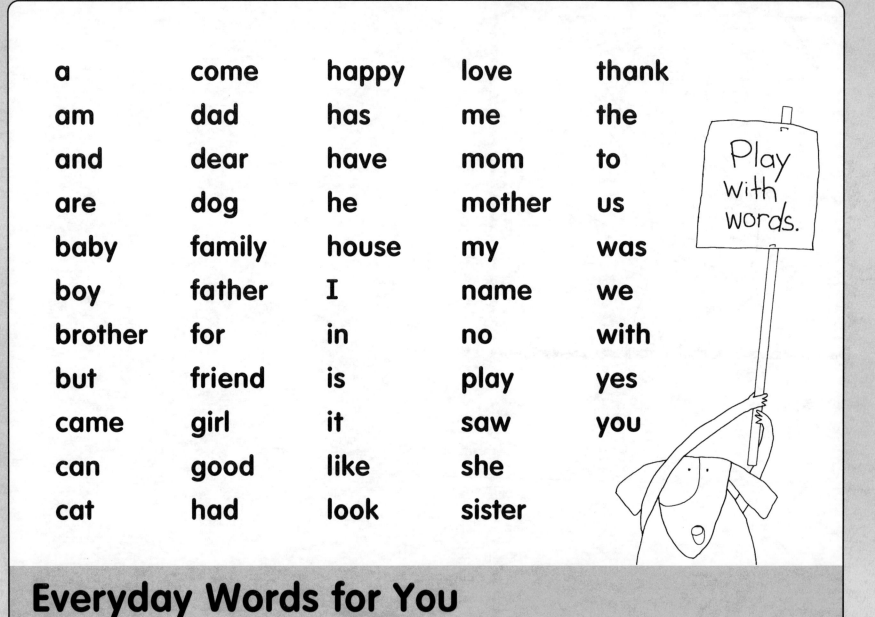

Play with words.

Everyday Words for You

Writers use everyday words to write stories.

Draw a picture. Then write a story about it. Use some words from the "Everyday Words for You" list if you wish.

Writers use everyday words to make sentences.

Write your name in the first sentence. Write three sentences about yourself.

My name is _____ .

_____

_____

_____